A Grayscale Coloring Book
All About
ANIME
32 PAGES WITH A VARIETY OF STYLES

Draconis
Publishing

ISBN: 978-1-989842-81-2

This book belongs to

CPSIA information can be obtained
at www.ICGtesting.com
Printed in the USA
LVHW061953301222
736161LV00031B/483